ASTERIX THE GAUL,
ASTERIX AND THE GOLDEN SICKLE,
ASTERIX AND THE GOTHS

Written by RENÉ GOSCINNY

Illustrated by ALBERT UDERZO

This omnibus © 2007 GOSCINNY/UDERZO

Exclusive licensee: Orion Publishing Group
Translators: Anthea Bell and Derek Hockridge
Typography: Bryony Newhouse

Asterix the Gaul
Original title: *Astérix le Gaulois*
© 1961 GOSCINNY/UDERZO
Revised edition and English translation © 2004 HACHETTE

Asterix and the Golden Sickle
Original title: *La Serpe d'or*
© 1962 GOSCINNY/UDERZO
Revised edition and English translation © 2004 HACHETTE

Asterix and the Goths
Original title: *Astérix et les Goths*
© 1963 GOSCINNY/UDERZO
Revised edition and English translation © 2004 HACHETTE

The right of René Goscinny and Albert Uderzo to be identified as the authors of this work
has been asserted by them in accordance with the Copyright, Designs and Patents Act 1988.

This edition first published in Great Britain in 2007 by
Orion Books Ltd,
Orion House, 5 Upper St Martin's Lane
London WC2H 9EA
An Hachette Livre UK Company

Printed in France

http://gb.asterix.com
www.orionbooks.co.uk

A CIP catalogue record for this book is available from the British Library

ISBN 978 0 7528 9154 5 (Hardback)
ISBN 978 0 7528 9155 2 (Trade Paperback)

The Orion Publishing Group's policy is to use papers that are natural, renewable and recyclable and made
from wood grown in sustainable forests. The logging and manufacturing processes are expected to conform to
the environmental regulations of the country of origin.

Every effort has been made to fulfil requirements with regard to reproducing copyright material.
The author and publisher will be glad to rectify any omissions at the earliest opportunity.

GAULISH VILLAGE

COMPENDIUM

LAUDANUM

AQUARIUM

TOTORUM

ARMORICA

BELGICA

LUTETIA

GAUL
(ROMAN CONQUEST)
50 BC

CELTICA

AQUITANIA

PROVINCIA

THE YEAR IS 50 BC. GAUL IS ENTIRELY OCCUPIED BY THE
ROMANS. WELL, NOT ENTIRELY ... ONE SMALL VILLAGE OF
INDOMITABLE GAULS STILL HOLDS OUT AGAINST THE INVADERS.
AND LIFE IS NOT EASY FOR THE ROMAN LEGIONARIES WHO
GARRISON THE FORTIFIED CAMPS OF TOTORUM, AQUARIUM,
LAUDANUM AND COMPENDIUM ...

ASTERIX, THE HERO OF THESE ADVENTURES. A SHREWD, CUNNING LITTLE WARRIOR, ALL PERILOUS MISSIONS ARE IMMEDIATELY ENTRUSTED TO HIM. ASTERIX GETS HIS SUPERHUMAN STRENGTH FROM THE MAGIC POTION BREWED BY THE DRUID GETAFIX . . .

OBELIX, ASTERIX'S INSEPARABLE FRIEND. A MENHIR DELIVERY MAN BY TRADE, ADDICTED TO WILD BOAR. OBELIX IS ALWAYS READY TO DROP EVERYTHING AND GO OFF ON A NEW ADVENTURE WITH ASTERIX – SO LONG AS THERE'S WILD BOAR TO EAT, AND PLENTY OF FIGHTING. HIS CONSTANT COMPANION IS DOGMATIX, THE ONLY KNOWN CANINE ECOLOGIST, WHO HOWLS WITH DESPAIR WHEN A TREE IS CUT DOWN.

GETAFIX, THE VENERABLE VILLAGE DRUID, GATHERS MISTLETOE AND BREWS MAGIC POTIONS. HIS SPECIALITY IS THE POTION WHICH GIVES THE DRINKER SUPERHUMAN STRENGTH. BUT GETAFIX ALSO HAS OTHER RECIPES UP HIS SLEEVE . . .

CACOFONIX, THE BARD. OPINION IS DIVIDED AS TO HIS MUSICAL GIFTS. CACOFONIX THINKS HE'S A GENIUS. EVERY-ONE ELSE THINKS HE'S UNSPEAKABLE. BUT SO LONG AS HE DOESN'T SPEAK, LET ALONE SING, EVERYBODY LIKES HIM . . .

FINALLY, VITALSTATISTIX, THE CHIEF OF THE TRIBE. MAJESTIC, BRAVE AND HOT-TEMPERED, THE OLD WARRIOR IS RESPECTED BY HIS MEN AND FEARED BY HIS ENEMIES. VITALSTATISTIX HIMSELF HAS ONLY ONE FEAR, HE IS AFRAID THE SKY MAY FALL ON HIS HEAD TOMORROW. BUT AS HE ALWAYS SAYS, TOMORROW NEVER COMES.

R. GOSCINNY *Asterix* A. UDERZO

Asterix
THE GAUL

Written by
René GOSCINNY

Illustrated by
Albert UDERZO

GOSCINNY AND UDERZO

PRESENT

An Asterix Adventure

ASTERIX
THE GAUL

Written by RENÉ GOSCINNY *and Illustrated by* ALBERT UDERZO

Translated by Anthea Bell *and* Derek Hockridge

IN THE YEAR 50 BC, AFTER A LONG STRUGGLE, THE ANCIENT GAULS HAD BEEN CONQUERED BY THE ROMANS...

CHIEFS LIKE VERCINGETORIX HAD TO LAY THEIR ARMS AT CAESAR'S FEET...

OUCH!

CLANG!

PEACE REIGNS, DISTURBED ONLY BY OCCASIONAL ATTACKS BY THE GERMANS, SPEEDILY REPULSED...

So! But ve komm back!

Gut! Ve go!

ALL GAUL IS OCCUPIED...

BELGICA

ARMORICA

CELTICA

AQUITANIA

PROVINCIA

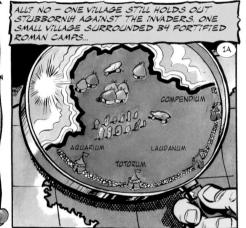

ALL? NO — ONE VILLAGE STILL HOLDS OUT STUBBORNLY AGAINST THE INVADERS. ONE SMALL VILLAGE SURROUNDED BY FORTIFIED ROMAN CAMPS...

1A

COMPENDIUM

AQUARIUM

LAUDANUM

TOTORUM

ALL EFFORTS TO SUBDUE THESE PROUD GAULS HAVE FAILED AND CAESAR ASKS HIMSELF...

QUID?

AND NOW WE MEET OUR HERO, THE WARRIOR ASTERIX, JUST OFF HUNTING AS USUAL...

BACK SOON, ASTERIX?

I'LL BE BACK FOR DINNER, OBELIX.

HERE HE COMES!

WE'LL GET HIM.

IPSO FACTO!

SIC!

BIFF!

OW!

BANG!

OUCH!

ACCIDENCE WILL HAPPEN...

VAE VICTO VAE VICTIS!

WE DECLINE!

1B

13

AND AT THE ROMAN CAMP OF COMPENDIUM, IN THE TENT OF CENTURION CRISMUS BONUS...

AVE CRISMUS BONUS! THE PATROLS BACK!

AVE JULIUS POMPUS! I'LL GO AND INSPECT THEM.

AVE...

?!???

WHAT HAPPENED, BY ALL THE GODS? WERE YOU ATTACKED BY SUPERIOR NUMBERS?

SUPERIOR NUMBERS...

CAN'T QUITE SAY...

THERE WAS ONE OF THEM...

NOT A VERY LARGE ONE EITHER!

2A

BY JUPITER! THERE MUST BE SOME SECRET BEHIND THE SUPERHUMAN STRENGTH OF THESE GAULS!

MEANWHILE ...

SO YOU'RE BACK, ASTERIX. ANYTHING INTERESTING HAPPEN?

NO...

OH YES! I KNOCKED FOUR ROMANS OUT.

OH, GOOD!

WANT TO HELP ME EAT MY BOAR?

JUST COMING! I'VE GOT TWO MORE MENHIRS TO DELIVER.

2B

COME IN, OBELIX. IT'S DONE TO A TURN!

YUM, YUM, ASTERIX!

THE ROMANS WON'T LIKE THIS. THEY'LL LAUNCH A NEW OFFENSIVE...

HUH!

SO LONG AS OUR DRUID GETAFIX KEEPS BREWING HIS MAGIC POTION, THE ROMANS CAN'T DO A THING.

LET'S GO AND SEE THE DRUID NOW!

TCHIC! TCHAC!

HE'LL BE UP THAT TREE, CUTTING MISTLETOE WITH HIS GOLDEN SICKLE.

3A

GETAFIX! O DRUID!

OWW!

YOU MADE ME JUMP! I'VE GONE AND CUT MYSELF WITH MY SICKLE.

SORRY...

THE TIME HAS COME FOR ME TO HAVE MY DOSE OF POTION...

OH, ALL RIGHT...

COME HOME WITH ME....

3B

15

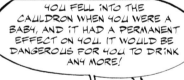

WE'VE BEEN LAYING SIEGE TO THESE GAULS FOR YEARS! THEY'VE GOT A NERVE! THIS MORNING'S PROVOCATION IS GOING TOO FAR. ONE AGAINST FOUR IS NO JOKE! THEY'RE MAKING US LOOK RIDICULOUS.

THERE'S SOME MYSTERY BEHIND THE STRENGTH OF THESE GAULS. WE MUST LEARN THEIR SECRET.

YOU'RE RIGHT, MARCUS GINANTONICUS! WE MUST LEARN THEIR SECRET, AND FAST! CAESAR HAS INDICATED HIS DISPLEASURE ALL THE WAY FROM ROME. WE NEED A SPY IN THE GAULS' VILLAGE. I WANT A VOLUNTEER!

?!

5A

AS THERE ARE SO MANY VOLUNTEERS, WE'LL HAVE TO PLAY MUSICAL CHAIRS TO PICK THE SPY!

THIS ANCIENT ROMAN GAME IS PLAYED WITH ONE CHAIR FEWER THAN THERE ARE LEGIONARIES...

...WHEN THE MUSIC STOPS...

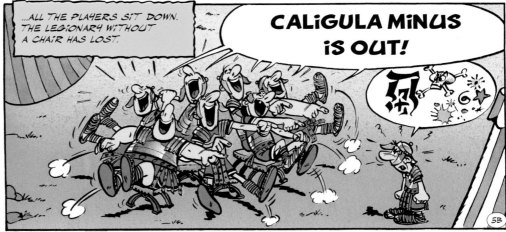

...ALL THE PLAYERS SIT DOWN. THE LEGIONARY WITHOUT A CHAIR HAS LOST.

CALIGULA MINUS IS OUT!

5B

17

18

(†) SPAGHETTI WAS NOT IMPORTED FROM CHINA BY MARCO POLO UNTIL MUCH LATER.

RIGHT! EVERYONE GOT IT? IF THEY ATTACK WE ONLY PUT UP A TOKEN RESISTANCE!

HERE WE COME, BY TOUTATIS!

HERE THEY COME, BY JUPITER!

9A

THEY'RE A BIT SOFT TODAY, DON'T YOU THINK?

YES, THEY'RE OFF FORM. THEY SHOULD TAKE CARE OF THEMSELVES — EAT A WELL BALANCED DIET.

PAF!

CLONG!

THAT'S THE LOT...

COULDN'T WE BRING THEM ROUND AND START AGAIN?

NO, COME ON! IT'S GETTING LATE.

Mi — MISSION ACCOMPLISHED!

WE WILL STRIKE OFF YOUR CHAINS!

BUT YOU'LL NEED TOOLS... A HAMMER!

HA! HA! WE'RE THE TOOLS!

!

WHAT'S YOUR NAME?

CALIG...ER...CALIGULIMINIX. I'M FROM LUTETIA. I WAS JUST GOING ON HOLIDAY TO ARMORICA WHEN THE ROMANS CAPTURED ME.

BUT EVERY-WHERE ELSE THE ROMANS AND THE GAULS ARE AT PEACE!

YES, BUT I LOOK SO CLEVER AND CUNNING THAT IN THEIR EYES I WAS A SPY.

THEIR EYES CAN'T BE ALL THAT BRIGHT! HA! HA!

9B

21

MARCUS GINANTONICUS AND HIS HEROIC DETACHMENT RETURN TO COMPENDIUM...

THE GAULS CAME AND SAW AND CONQUERED CALIGULA MINUS!

10A

A GREAT VICTORY FOR US!

LET'S HOPE CALIGULA MINUS GETS BACK IN ONE PIECE TO TELL US WHAT HE'S SEEN!

HE'D BETTER! IF NOT I'LL HAVE SOMETHING TO SAY TO HIS ROMAN REMAINS!

ALEA JACTA EST!

PARDON?

MEANWHILE...

THIS IS OUR VILLAGE, CALIGULIMINIX. YOU'LL BE SAFE HERE! IT'S FULL OF GAULS!

THAT'S A GREAT COMFORT.

ASTERIX AND OBELIX ARE BACK!

THEY'VE GOT SOMETHING WITH THEM!

SOMETHING VERY PECULIAR, BY BELENOS!

COME AND MEET OUR CHIEF VITALSTATISTIX.

BUT – BUT THEY'RE ALL ARMED!

YES, WE HAVE TO BE PREPARED TO FIGHT THE ROMANS AT THE DROP OF A HELMET.

A WISE PRECAUTION!

10B

DINNER'S READY, CALIGULIMINIX. IT'S WILD BOAR!

IS THERE SOME SECRET BEHIND YOUR SUPERHUMAN STRENGTH?

YUM! YUM! YES BUT WE CAN'T REVEAL IT! SCRUNCH!

EAT UP YOUR BOAR, IT'S GETTING COLD.

WHY CAN'T YOU REVEAL YOUR SECRET?

BECAUSE IT'S A SECRET!

THAT'S NOT FAIR! WHAT ARE THINGS COMING TO IF ONE GAUL CAN'T TRUST ANOTHER?

?

IF I WAS AS STRONG AS YOU I COULD GET THROUGH THE ROMAN LINES AND GO HOME TO LUTETIA!

!

12A

MY POOR FAMILY! SNIFF! THEY'LL BE WORRIED TO DEATH!

WHAT DO WE DO NOW?

WE COULD ALWAYS EAT HIS WILD BOAR?

COME ON, CALIGULIMINIX! WE'RE GOING TO SEE THE DRUID.

HE'LL BE UP AN OAK TREE. IT'S THE SIXTH DAY OF THE NEW MOON, AND MISTLETOE CUT THEN IS A POWERFUL ANTIDOTE TO POISON.

HI, DRUID!

OUCH!

ASTERIX, I TOLD YOU BEFORE NOT TO MAKE ME JUMP WHEN I'M USING MY SICKLE!!!

12B

WELL, WHAT DO YOU WANT?

I DON'T WANT ANYTHING. IT'S MY FRIEND CALIGULIMINIX – HE'D LIKE TO KNOW THE SECRET OF OUR SUPER-HUMAN STRENGTH...

NOTHING DOING!

!

I HAVE TO GET HOME TO MY FAMILY ... GO BACK TO WORK ...

13A

WHAT DO YOU DO, ANYWAY?

ER... OH, I'M A GUIDE. I SHOW BARBARIAN TOURISTS ROUND THE NIGHT LIFE OF LUTETIA...

WELL, WHAT ABOUT IT, DRUID?

NO, NO, AND FOR THE THIRD TIME, **NO!**

OH, FINE! THAT'S JUST FINE! I QUITE SEE!

I'LL TRY GOING HOME ALL THE SAME. AND IF THE ROMANS TAKE ME TO ROME FOR THE LIONS TO EAT ME IN THE CIRCUS, I'LL SAY IN BETWEEN EACH MOUTHFUL THE LIONS TAKE, 'IT'S ALL GETAFIX THE DRUID'S FAULT! IT'S ALL GETAFIX THE DRUID'S FAULT!'

OH, ALL RIGHT, ALL RIGHT!

COME BACK, CALIGULIMINIX!

I'LL SHOW YOU MY SECRET. I'LL EVEN LET YOU TASTE IT.

IT'S A SECRET YOU CAN EAT?

13B

THIS IS GREAT!

KERPLONK!

THE POTION MAKES YOU VERY STRONG, BUT NOT INVULNERABLE... I DO HAVE A RECIPE FOR THAT, BUT THAT'S ANOTHER STORY...

AND NOW I DECLARE THE REVELS OPEN!

HI, CACOFONIX, WE'RE WAITING FOR YOU!

COME ON, TENANSIX!

WHAT ARE WE GOING TO DO NOW?

DANCE!

15A

TAKE YOUR PARTNERS! SET TO THE RIGHT — SET TO THE LEFT...

ONE LINE FORWARD, THE OTHER LINE BACK!

SET TO YOUR PARTNER, SHAKE HIM BY THE HAND!

PULL HIS MOUSTACHE!

PULL HIS MOUSTACHE! ?!?

?

15B

30

SOON AFTERWARDS IN THE GAULISH VILLAGE...

WANT ME TO COME WITH YOU, DRUID?

I'M JUST GOING TO PICK SOME MISTLETOE IN THE FOREST.

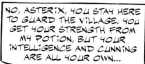

NO, ASTERIX, YOU STAY HERE TO GUARD THE VILLAGE. YOU GET YOUR STRENGTH FROM MY POTION, BUT YOUR INTELLIGENCE AND CUNNING ARE ALL YOUR OWN...

IT WOULD BE A DISASTER FOR US TO LOSE YOU! BESIDES, I'LL BE BACK SOON.

GOOD...

♪ (1)

(1) ANCIENT GAULISH AIR

OOPS!

GOT HIM!

19A

⚡✴✊💀 (2)

(2) ANCIENT GAULISH SWEAR-WORDS

SOON AFTERWARDS...

WE GOT THE DRUID, O CRISMUS BONUS!

GOOD WORK, TULLIUS OCTOPUS!

AS A REWARD YOU SHALL HAVE 100 SESTERTII, AND YOU CAN GO TO ROME ON LEAVE TO SEE THE CIRCUS!

GOODY GOODY GUMDROPS! I'M GOING TO THE CIRCUS!

NOW, DRUID, YOU WILL TELL ME YOUR SECRET!

THAT'S WHAT YOU THINK!

19B

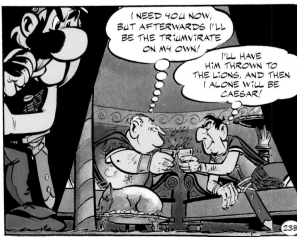

MOST INTERESTING, BUT IT TELLS ME NOTHING OF GETAFIX'S WHEREABOUTS!

HE MUST BE IN THAT HEAVILY GUARDED TENT...

THE BOLD APPROACH!

DO YOU MIND? I'VE JUST COME TO RESCUE GETAFIX THE DRUID. HE'S A FRIEND OF MINE.

?! ?!

THANKS!

24A

DON'T LET HIM OUT! HE'S ONE OF THOSE INVINCIBLE GAULS... MAGIC POTION FAIRLY OOZING OUT OF HIS EARS! I'M GOING FOR REINFORCEMENTS!

V...VERY WELL! BUT DON'T BE LONG, O CAIUS FLEBITUS!

AND INSIDE THE TENT...

ASTERIX!

ALL WELL?

BY BELISAMA, ASTERIX! WHAT MADNESS TO VENTURE RIGHT INTO THE JAWS OF THE ROMAN WOLF!

THE ROMANS CAN'T DO A THING AGAINST MY MAGIC POWERS!

EXACTLY! WE'LL HAVE SOME FUN WITH THEM! I'VE GOT A FEW IDEAS!

SIR! SIR!

24B

SEIZE HIM, YOU LILY-LIVERED LOT, OR I'LL SEND YOU TO THE CIRCUS TO BE THROWN TO THE LIONS!

THE CIRCUS?

THE LIONS?

OH WELL!

CLINK!

CLANK!

CLONK!

CLUNK!

WHAT'S UP?

IT'S A GAUL WHO GOT INTO THE CAMP...

26A

IT'S NOT FAIR! HE DIDN'T WAIT FOR ME TO WAKE UP TO PLAY HIS PRACTICAL JOKE! IT'S NOT FAIR!

?

YOU REFUSED TO TALK, DRUID, BUT PERHAPS YOUR FRIEND WILL PROVE MORE LOQUACIOUS UNDER TORTURE TOMORROW!

AUT CAESAR, AUT NIHIL! (¹)

(¹) THIS IS LATIN GRAMMAR.

HA! HA! HA! HA! HA! HA! HA!

I'LL BE LOQUACIOUS ALL RIGHT! I'LL LOQUACE LIKE NO ONE EVER LOQUACED BEFORE! (¹)

(¹) THIS IS BAD GRAMMAR.

26B

38

39

IT'S DAYS SINCE THE MESSENGERS LEFT TO LOOK FOR STRAWBERRIES, AND NOT ONE HAS TURNED UP YET!

THE MESSENGERS ARE BACK, O CRISMUS BONUS!

ABOUT TIME!

AVE CRISMUS BONUS!

AVE, AVE, BOYS! THE STRAWBERRIES — DID YOU GET THEM?

NO.

NOT A STRAWBERRY.

WE LOOKED EVERYWHERE!

TULLIUS OCTOPUS ISN'T BACK YET.

29A

HERE I AM, O CRISMUS BONUS!

I FOUND STRAWBERRIES, O CRISMUS BONUS! I BOUGHT THEM FOR A VAST SUM FROM A GREEK MERCHANT I HAPPENED TO MEET!

GIVE THEM HERE!

THIS TIME I REALLY MEAN IT! AS A REWARD YOU CAN GO HOME ON LEAVE TO SEE ALL THE FUN OF THE CIRCUS!

I'M GOING TO THE CIRCUS! I'M GOING TO THE CIRCUS!

DRUID! HERE ARE THE STRAWBERRIES YOU ORDERED FOR THE MAGIC POTION!

WHAT DO YOU THINK OF THEM, ASTERIX?

NOT UP TO MUCH!

!

NOT BAD...

HM...

COME TO THINK OF IT, THOSE WERE EXCELLENT STRAWBERRIES!

YES, JUST THE SORT I NEED. GO AND GET ME SOME MORE.

29B

42

31A

4.60

31B

43

WELL, IF YOU DON'T NEED ME ANY MORE I'LL BE OFF...

GEE UP!

33A

WAIT A MINUTE! IF I GOT IT RIGHT, I'M VERY STRONG NOW!

THIS IS GREAT! NOW I CAN SELL MY OXEN AND PULL THE CART MYSELF!

THAT POTION...

...CERTAINLY DOES HAVE...

...MAGIC POWERS!

AND AT COMPENDIUM...

GLUG GLUG GLUG GLUG!

COME ON, EVERYONE! LET'S ALL DRINK THE MAGIC POTION!

33B

48

49

I GIVE IN! GIVE ME THE ANTIDOTE AND YOU CAN GO FREE!

TRY A HAIR OF THE DOG?

GETAFIX MAY NOT REMEMBER THE ANTIDOTE...

HE'S A BIT HARE-BRAINED SOMETIMES!

HO! HO! HO!

POF! POF!

DON'T DISTRESS YOURSELF! WE AGREE!

I'LL HAVE TO GO AND FETCH INGREDIENTS FROM THE FOREST...

I'LL ARRANGE FOR AN ESCORT...

!

I MAY NOT HAVE THE SECRET OF THE MAGIC POTION, BUT AS SOON AS I'VE GOT RID OF THIS HAIR I'LL WIPE OUT THOSE TWO GAULS. IT WILL GIVE ME MORAL SATISFACTION!

38A

WHY WERE YOU SO QUICK TO ACCEPT HIS OFFER? THAT CENTURION MEANS MISCHIEF!

THE EFFECTS OF THE HAIR LOTION DON'T LAST LONG...

TOMORROW THEIR HAIR WILL HAVE STOPPED GROWING. I MUST THINK OF A WAY OUT OF THIS!

REPORTING TO ESCORT YOU TO THE FOREST FOR INGREDIENTS!

STOP WALKING ON MY HAIR!

WELL, PICK IT UP, THEN!

I HAVE A PLAN!

THAT'S OUR STRONG POINT, WE'RE BURSTING WITH IDEAS!

38B

R. GOSCINNY ASTERIX A. UDERZO

Asterix and the
Golden Sickle

Written by
René GOSCINNY

Illustrated by
Albert UDERZO

LUTETIA

GOSCINNY AND UDERZO
PRESENT
An Asterix Adventure

ASTERIX
AND THE
GOLDEN SICKLE

Written by RENÉ GOSCINNY *and Illustrated by* ALBERT UDERZO

Translated by Anthea Bell *and* Derek Hockridge

THE FIERCELY INDEPENDENT LITTLE VILLAGE WHERE ASTERIX AND THE OTHER GAULS LIVE IS AT PEACE...

GOOD HUNTING, ASTERIX?

NOTHING MUCH TODAY...

OBELIX IS HAPPILY AT WORK, CARVING OUT A MENHIR...

THERE'LL ALWAYS BE A GAU-AAUL... ♪ ♫

CACOFONIX THE BARD IS GIVING THE CHILDREN LESSONS...

WELL, YOUNG MAN, AND INTO HOW MANY PARTS IS GAUL DIVIDED?

?

$VIII \times V = XL$

$\dfrac{III}{+ \dfrac{I}{= IV}}$

IN SHORT, EVERYONE IS CONTENTED. ALL IS PEACE AND PLENTY...

ANOTHER BOAR, OBELIX?

YES, PLEASE!

WHEN SUDDENLY...

OH, BY TOUTATIS!

??

?

?

THANK YOU FOR OFFERING ASTERIX, BUT I REALLY COULDN'T LET YOU GO OFF TO LUTETIA...

I INSIST, O DRUID.

IT'S FAR TOO DANGEROUS!

OH, WELL, IN THAT CASE...

!

ER... RIGHT! I ACCEPT!

OH!

I'M COMING TOO! METALLURGIX IS A DISTANT COUSIN OF MINE. HE'S THE BIG SUCCESS IN OUR FAMILY.

LET'S GET GOING STRAIGHT AWAY!

I'LL TELL THE OTHERS!

3-A

BY TOUTATIS AND BELENOS, I WISH YOU A GOOD JOURNEY AND A SPEEDY RETURN WITH A FINE GOLDEN SICKLE FOR OUR DRUID.

YOU CAN COUNT ON US, O CHIEF VITALSTATISTIX!

HERE'S A SPOT OF MAGIC POTION. IT WILL MAKE YOU INVINCIBLE EVERY TIME YOU DRINK IT!

THANKS...

I WILL NOW GIVE YOU A SONG OF FAREWELL...

GOODBYE...

IT'S GETTING LATE...

I'VE GOT A WILD BOAR ON THE SPIT...

LATER...

WHAT'S THAT MENHIR FOR?

IT'S A PRESENT FOR METALLURGIX. JUST A LITTLE GIFT AS A TOKEN OF FRIENDSHIP...

3-B

NEXT MORNING...

Auf wiedersehen!

The Cont Barbaria

HEY, ASTERIX, WHY DO YOU THINK THAT TRAVELLER TOLD US SICKLES WERE IN SHORT SUPPLY IN LUTETIA?

NO IDEA, OBELIX.

LET'S ENJOY OUR JOURNEY; WE CAN WORRY ABOUT THAT LATER...

THE ROMANS ARE RUINING THE LANDSCAPE WITH ALL THESE MODERN BUILDINGS!

OUR FRIENDS' JOURNEY PROCEEDS WITHOUT MUCH INCIDENT, APART FROM A FEW SCUFFLES WITH BANDITS...

AT SUINDINUM, ASTERIX AND OBELIX ARE UNABLE TO FIND A BED, AS IT HAPPENS TO BE THE DAY OF THE GREAT OX-CART RACE, THE SUINDINUM 24 HOURS...

BUT AT LAST, ONE DAY...

LOOK! OBELIX!

LUTETIA!

ISN'T IT BIG!

66

WHAT DO YOU WANT?

I'VE COME TO WARN YOU THERE ARE TWO MEN LOOKING FOR METALLURGIX.

METALLURGIX? WELL, WELL... AND WHAT ARE THESE MEN LIKE?

NO SPECIAL DISTINGUISHING MARKS. A FAT GAUL AND A LITTLE GAUL...

OH YES, I FORGOT. ONE OF THEM CARRIES A MENHIR ABOUT WITH HIM.

A MENHIR?

RIGHT. CLEAR OFF, AND KEEP YOUR MOUTH SHUT IF YOU WANT TO STAY ALIVE!

DON'T WORRY. I'LL BE DUMB AS A DOLMEN!

NOW TO TRY AND FIND THOSE TWO NOSEY PARKERS...

10.A

BY BELENOS, I THINK I'M IN LUCK!

THIS IS SERIOUS. IF OUR DRUID IS TO ATTEND THE CONFERENCE IN THE FOREST OF THE CARNUTES, WE MUST GET HOLD OF A SICKLE FOR HIM. IT'S URGENT!

AND WE MUST GET HOLD OF A BOAR FOR ME. THAT'S URGENT TOO...

YOU MAKE ME SICK, GOING ON ABOUT BOARS ALL THE TIME!

AND YOU BORE ME GOING ON ABOUT SICKLES!

10.B

71

72

73

AVE, O SURPLUS DAIRIPRODUS.

AVE, OLD CHAP, AVE...

WHO ARE THESE PEOPLE DISTURBING MY MEAL?

GAULS. SOME GAULS HAVE BEEN HAVING A PUNCH-UP.

I'M TIRED OF GAULS. THEY'RE ALWAYS FIGHTING. IT'S SUCH A BORE...

THESE TWO GAULS HAVE BROKEN UP NAVISHTRIX'S PLACE.

HAD A DROP TOO MUCH BEER, EH?

NO. WE WERE JUST TRYING TO BUY A GOLDEN SICKLE FOR OUR DRUID.

I ALWAYS THOUGHT NAVISHTRIX WAS MIXED UP IN THIS SICKLE-TRAFFICKING BUSINESS...

HOW VERY PERSPICACIOUS OF YOU, O SURPLUS DAIRIPRODUS.

ALL RIGHT, ALL RIGHT. RELEASE THESE GAULS, I FIND THEM TIRING... WHAT A BORE, WHAT A BORE...

WHAT IS ALL THIS ABOUT A SICKLE-TRAFFICKING BUSINESS?

OH, THERE'S A GANG OF GOLDEN-SICKLE-TRAFFICKERS IN LUTETIA. SICKLES ARE IN GREAT DEMAND, BECAUSE OF THE CONFERENCE IN THE FOREST OF THE CARNUTES...

WHAT DID HE MEAN, WHAT A BOAR? I CAN'T SEE ONE ANYWHERE...

SO NOW THEY HAVE THE MONOPOLY, ESPECIALLY AS METALLURGIX DISAPPEARED WITHOUT LEAVING ANY FORWARDING ADDRESS...

BUT THEN... PERHAPS THEY'VE KIDNAPPED METALLURGIX?

KIDNAPPED OR MURDERED... WELL, OFF YOU GO, AND I DON'T WANT TO SEE ANY MORE OF YOU!

BOOOHOOOO! POOR COUSIN METALLURGIX!

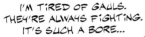

THE SUN, RISING ON LUTETIA, IS GREETED BY A COCKEREL...

COCK-A-DOODLE-DO!

GET UP, OBELIX! IT'S TIME TO START OUR INVESTIGATIONS!

THAT'S RIGHT. WE MUST FIND METALLURGIX.

LET'S GO BACK TO THAT ARVERNIAN IN THE WINE SHOP. I'M SURE HE KNOWS SOMETHING!

THE SUN OF MASSILIA

OH!

COULD YOU TELL US WHERE TO FIND THE ARVERNIAN WHO...

OH, I EXPECT YOU MEAN THE FORMER PROPRIETOR?

THAT CRAZY GAUL WHO SOLD ME THIS PLACE FOR A HANDFUL OF BRONZE COINS! IT'S UNDER NEW MANAGEMENT NOW, BUT YOU WON'T BE DISAPPOINTED!

I CAN OFFER YOU MY SPECIALITY: FISH SOUP! MADE OF NICE FRESH FISH, JUST ARRIVED BY OX-CART FROM MASSILIA!

DO YOU KNOW WHERE THE ARVERNIAN HAS GONE?

OH! HE STARTED FOR GERGOVIA THIS MORNING, TRAVELLING BY OX-CART, THE SAME AS THE FISH!

THE SUN OF MASSILIA

WHAT A SHAME! IF YOU'D COME A LITTLE SOONER YOU'D HAVE FOUND HIM STILL HERE!

THANKS!

ALL THESE LUTETIANS ARE CRAZY, BY BELISAMA!

81

82

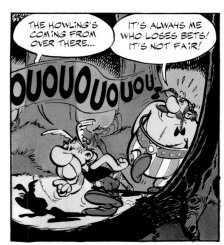

86

87

WARM RAYS OF BRILLIANT SUNSHINE LIGHT UP A CLOUDLESS SKY...

...LITTLE BIRDS WARBLE ON THE LEAFY BRANCHES...

...SQUIRRELS PLAY ON THE MOSSY GROUND...

...WHILE UNDERNEATH THE MOSSY GROUND...

'PLAF!
OUCH!
BOING
KEEEH
BOUM!

GET THEM, OBELIX!

YOU BET I WILL, ASTERIX!

ARE THERE ANY LEFT, ASTERIX?

NO, OBELIX, YOU'RE JUST FINISHING OFF THE LAST ONE...

BONG!
BONG!
BONG!

LET'S GET OUT OF HERE AND WARN THE BOSS!

OBELIX, I'M A BIT WORRIED... I CAN'T FIND NAVISHTRIX!

HE CAN'T HAVE COME TO ANY HARM. HE WAS HERE JUST NOW!

ANYWAY, I'VE GOT CLOVOGARLIX.

THAT'S SOMETHING...

92

93

95

98

101

GOSCINNY Asterix A. UDERZO

Asterix and the Goths

Written by René GOSCINNY   Illustrated by Albert UDERZO

GOSCINNY AND UDERZO
PRESENT
An Asterix Adventure

ASTERIX AND THE GOTHS

Written by RENÉ GOSCINNY *and Illustrated by* ALBERT UDERZO

Translated by Anthea Bell *and* Derek Hockridge

109

110

IT'S A JOLLY GOOD JOB WE DID COME WITH YOU, GETAFIX, WITH ALL THESE BARBARIANS PROWLING AROUND!

HUH! WARS BETWEEN BARBARIANS AND ROMANS ARE NO CONCERN OF OURS...

FOREST OF THE CARNUTES NON-DRUIDS KEEP OUT

AH, WE'RE THERE!

RIGHT, WE'LL WAIT HERE UNTIL THE CONFERENCE IS OVER.

VERY WELL.

GOOD LUCK IN THE COMPETITION!

LET'S MAKE OURSELVES COMFORTABLE...

I WONDER WHAT THE BARBARIANS ARE DOING AROUND HERE...

THIS IS A GOOD SPOT... PLENTY OF WILD BOAR ABOUT!

AND NOT FAR AWAY...

WELL, MEN, YOU KNOW WHY WE'RE HERE...

Our mission is to capture the best Gaulish druid. We'll take him back across the border, and then, with the help of his magic, we'll plan the invasion of Gaul and Rome...

To the greater glory of the Visigoths, the Ostrogoths, and any other sort of Goths!

Long live Choleric, our chief!

Silence! Let's eavesdrop on the conference and capture the druid who wins first prize!

DO YOU KNOW, VALUADDETAX, I FEEL SURE I'M GOING TO WIN FIRST PRIZE AND BE ELECTED DRUID OF THE YEAR!

⑤

111

THE FOREST OF THE CARNUTES IS SWARMING WITH DRUIDS IN MERRY MOOD ALL DELIGHTED TO SEE EACH OTHER AGAIN...

EVERY OAK TREE IS FULL OF DRUIDS HARD AT WORK CUTTING MISTLETOE WITH THEIR SICKLES...

SNIP!
SNIP!

OOOOUCH! THAT'S MY FINGER!

SWISH!

THEY TALK SHOP, THEY DISCUSS SPELLS...

YES, MY DEAR FELLOW, I PICKED UP THIS SICKLE IN A LITTLE SHOP IN DARIORIGUM! LOOK, IT'S GOT A SAFETY-CATCH.

SO THEN, OLD MAN, HEY PRESTO! I TURNED HIM INTO A MENHIR!

THEY EVEN INDULGE IN JOKES AND PUNS... IN SHORT, THEY ARE HAVING A GOOD TIME

THIS FOOD'S A BIT SICKLE-Y!

PASS ME THE CELT!

IT MUST BE HIS GAUL-BLADDER!

MENHIR A TRUE WORD IS SPOKEN IN JEST!

THEN, AFTER THE GREAT BANQUET...

SILENCE, BROTHERS, SILENCE!

CLANG!
CLANG!
CLANG!

BROTHER DRUIDS, THE TIME HAS COME FOR US TO BEGIN OUR GREAT CONTEST TO EVALUATE NEW METHODS AND ELECT THE DRUID OF THE YEAR...

AND WHILE THE DRUIDS PREPARE THEIR MAGIC POTIONS...

...GREEDY EYES ARE WATCHING THEM...

Now comes the interesting part!

6

FIRST CANDIDATE... DRUID BOTANIX!

JUST A FEW DROPS OF POTION ON THE GROUND...

CLAP! CLAP! CLAP!

...AND THERE YOU HAVE MAGNIFICENT OUT-OF-SEASON FLOWERS!

CLAP! CLAP!

QUITE CHARMING!

HOW DELIGHTFUL...

CLAP! CLAP!

CLAP! CLAP! CLAP!

Shut up, you idiot!

What's up? I can like flowers even if I am a barbarian, can't I?

Hmmmff!

CANDIDATE NUMBER TWO: DRUID PREFIX!

I JUST THROW SOME POWDER IN THE AIR...

...AND I MAKE IT RAIN!

NOT BAD!

THE WEATHER'S ALL TOPSY-TURVY THESE DAYS!

DRUID SUFFIX!

KTISHOO!

PARP!

I HAVE INVENTED A METHOD OF MAKING POWDERED SOUP SO THAT IT CAN BE CARRIED ABOUT IN LITTLE PACKETS. MUCH LESS BOTHER THAN A CAULDRON!

BUT TO MAKE IT INTO SOUP YOU STILL NEED A CAULDRON...

I'VE THOUGHT OF EVERYTHING, O VENERABLE CHIEF DRUID...

I'VE INVENTED A METHOD OF MAKING POWDERED CAULDRONS TOO!

WELL DONE!

HOW INGENIOUS!

VERY CLEVER!

CLAP! CLAP!

CLAP! CLAP!

THE COMPETITION'S BEGUN. THEY SEEM TO BE ENJOYING THEMSELVES!

YOU MARK MY WORDS, OBELIX! I'M CERTAIN OUR DRUID WILL WIN FIRST PRIZE WITH HIS MAGIC POTION.

NON-DRUIDS KEEP OUT

BRAVO! CLAP!

CLAP! CLAP!

7

AND NOW WE COME TO THE NEXT CANDIDATE, VALUADDETAX!

I HAVE BREWED A POTION WHICH MAKES YOU IMMUNE TO PAIN! JUST WATCH THIS...

GLUG! GLUG! GLUG!

...AND NOW I CAN TAKE CHIPS OUT OF BOILING OIL WITH MY BARE HANDS!!

VERY PRACTICAL!

GREAT.

CLAP!

CLAP!

CLAP! CLAP! CLAP! CLAP!

CLA...

AND NOW OUR LAST CANDIDATE... DRUID GETAFIX!

I SHOULD LIKE TO DEMONSTRATE MY POTION WHICH GIVES A MAN SUPERHUMAN STRENGTH!

I NEED THE HELP OF A FEEBLE DRUID!

I'M A FEEBLE DRUID...

DRINK THIS, AND THEN GO AND UPROOT AN OAK TREE, FEEBLE DRUID!

THIS ONE?

EEEEEK! OOOOOH!

CRAAACK!

ARE YOU OUT OF YOUR MIND?

HEY, CAN'T YOU LET US CUT MISTLETOE IN PEACE?!!

I HAD ALREADY HEARD ABOUT YOUR POTION, GETAFIX, BUT IT'S EVEN MORE IMPRESSIVE THAN I'D BEEN LED TO BELIEVE!

CAN I GO NOW?

HURRAH! HE'S THE WINNER!

That's the one we want!

8

114

117

118

122

AS SOON AS THE ROMANS KNOW THAT THE GOTHS THEY ARE LOOKING FOR ARE DISGUISED AS ROMANS THERE IS COMPLETE CHAOS... THE ROMANS GO ABOUT CAPTURING ONE ANOTHER...

I'M TAKING YOU IN, GOTH!

YOU OFF YOUR HEAD OR SOMETHING?

I'M A ROMAN! I'M A ROMAN! I'M A ROMAN!

GOT YOU, YOU BARBARIAN!

THE UNHAPPY GENERAL CANTANKERUS IS NEARLY OUT OF HIS MIND...

THEY'RE ALL QUITE THICK, AND I'M THEIR LEADER! (SOB! SOB!)

BUT SOME PEOPLE ARE MAKING THE MOST OF THE SITUATION, FOR INSTANCE, ASTERIX AND OBELIX, WHO HAVE PUT THEIR OWN CLOTHES ON AGAIN...

...AND THE GOTHS, THE ROOT OF ALL THE TROUBLE, WHO ARE PROCEEDING UNEVENTFULLY TOWARDS THEIR OWN COUNTRY OF GERMANIA.

Watch out! The frontier's ahead. We've got to cross it!

A HEAVY RESPONSIBILITY WEIGHS ON THOSE WHO GUARD THE FRONTIER AGAINST FOREIGN INVADERS...

GAUL
ROMAN EMPIRE

Germania

Hey!

MMMM?

BONG!

Victory is ours! We'll be given a hero's welcome by our own people!

Anything to declare?

18

You bet we've got something to declare! One druid!

Will you open the parcel, please.

* GAULISH SWEAR-WORDS WHICH WE DECLINE TO TRANSLATE.

You realise you're importing foreign goods...

That was our mission — to bring back a druid to help us get ready for the next invasion. Let us through, you stupid Ostrogoth!

Oh no! You'll have to see the C.O.

* GOTHIC SWEAR-WORDS WHICH MAY BE TRANSLATED INTO GAULISH AS FOLLOWS:

MEANWHILE, ON THE OTHER SIDE OF THE BORDER...

WHAT'S ALL THIS, LEGIONARY? ASLEEP ON GUARD DUTY?

Germania
ROMAN EMPIRE

I WAS ATTACKED FROM THE REAR BY SOME GOTHS WHO WERE INVADING THE GOTHS...

A LIKELY STORY! GOTHS INVADING GAUL, ALL RIGHT, GAULS INVADING THE GOTHS, ALL RIGHT...

GAUL
ROMAN EMPIRE

BUT GOTHS INVADING THE GOTHS, THAT'S STUPID!!!

BUT I TELL YOU...

SOON AFTERWARDS...

COME ON! WE MUST CROSS THE BORDER AND INVADE GERMANIA!

I HOPE THEY'VE GOT BOARS IN GERMANIA.

THE CENTURION JUST DOESN'T WANT TO KNOW!

GAUL
ROMAN EMPIRE

19

126

128

ASTERIX AND OBELIX ARE NOT THE ONLY ONES WITH ESCAPE IN MIND FOR IN ANOTHER PART OF THE TOWN...

I'LL GO TO GAUL. WITH MY KNOWLEDGE OF MODERN LANGUAGES I'LL BE ABLE TO GET A JOB THERE...

Halt! Who goes there?

THE PATROL!

Well, if it isn't Rhetoric the interpreter! And where might you be off to at this time of night?

Well, I... er... the fact is... well, it was like this, you see...

No, I don't! It's the guardroom for you! You can explain yourself tomorrow!

No, no! You're making a big mistake! I've got friends in high places!!!

I'M DONE FOR! THE CHIEF WILL NEVER FORGIVE ME FOR DECEIVING HIM ABOUT WHAT THAT PIG-HEADED DRUID SAID...

MEANWHILE...

GOT IT? NO FIGHTING, AND NO TALKING TO ANY GOTHS.

RIGHT!

EEEK! THAT'S TORN IT!

Hello, hello, hello! Who have we here? You're for the guardroom too!

25

131

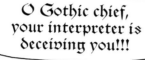

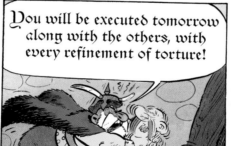

136

138

Let's go and get the prisoners... it's time for the execution.

They've gone very quiet... I've never known condemned men so quiet before.

They won't be so quiet in a few minutes!

B² B³ B⁴

YOU'VE SUNK A GALLEY. ✻

THERE'S SOMEONE COMING.

✻ THIS GAME, QUINQUIREMES AND GALLEYS, IS STILL PLAYED DURING LESSONS TODAY, THOUGH THE PLAYERS, IF DISCOVERED, MAY FIND THEMSELVES IN DIRE STRAITS.

Your time has come!

HURRY UP! HURRY UP!

WE'LL FINISH THE GAME LATER.

They... they seem to be in a hurry!

?

CIRCUS
← Stage door

Go on!

Bravo!
Hurrah!
Begin!

Now, everyone listen to me! I've got some of the Gaulish druid's magic powers! I'm your new chief, Rhetoric I!

That's the stuff! Down with Metric!

Hurrah! Long live Rhetoric I!

PLATCH!

CLAP! CLAP! CLAP!

Just a minute! I'm the chief around here!

Throw this poor fish into the dungeons! It's time you were going, Metric.

SOON AFTERWARDS, IN THE PALACE...

COME ALONG IN, FRIENDS, COME ALONG IN. I WAS JUST PLANNING THE PROGRAMME FOR METRIC'S TORTURE TOMORROW.

What were we saying?

Well, and then we could put him in a double saucepan and stir over a slow flame...

SORRY TO INTERRUPT YOU, RHETORIC, BUT WE HAVE A FAVOUR TO ASK YOU...

YES? ANYTHING YOU LIKE, MY DEAR ASTERIX!

WE WANT TO VISIT METRIC IN HIS DUNGEON, TO CROW OVER HIM...

AN EXCELLENT IDEA! OFF YOU GO! HAVE A NICE TIME!

IT'S STILL WORKING!

When these Gauls have served their purpose I'll have to get rid of them...

I've got something special for them: a pressure cooker. It can cook a person in a couple of minutes, and it whistles when he's done!

Hee, hee! You can't stop progress!

36

ASTERIX, GETAFIX AND OBELIX MAKE THEIR WAY BACK TO THE DUNGEON FOR A WORD WITH METRIC...

Metric, would you like to get your revenge on Rhetoric and return to power?

?

HE SAYS YES!

I GOT THE GENERAL IDEA!

Have a swig of this magic potion... then you'll be as strong as Rhetoric. The way you use your strength is up to you...

!

GLUG! GLUG!

CLINNNK!

HE'S GOT A FREE HAND NOW!

CRAAAASH!

Here we go again! They ought to replace that door with a curtain!

Raise the alarm! The prisoner's escaping!!!

So what?

POC!

HE'S GOT A FREE HAND! HA! HA! HA! THAT'S A GOOD ONE, THAT IS! I'VE ONLY JUST GOT IT. HO! HO! HO!

37

THE ASTERIXIAN WARS

A Tangled Web...

The ruse employed by Asterix, Getafix and Obelix succeeded beyond their wildest dreams. After drinking the druid's magic potion, the Goths fought each other tooth and nail. Here is a brief summary to help you follow the history of these famous wars.

Metric

Rhetoric

The favourite and devastating weapon of the combatants.

Diagram indicating the course of events.

The first victory is won outright by Rhetoric, who, having surprised Metric by an outflanking movement, lets him have it – bonk! – and inflicts a crushing defeat on him. This defeat, however, is only temporary...

Rhetoric has no time to celebrate his victory, for, having completed his outflanking movement, he is taken in the rear by his own ally, Lyric. Lyric instantly proclaims himself supreme chief of all the Goths, much to the amusement of the other chiefs...

Who turn out to be right, for Lyric's brother-in-law Satiric lays an ambush for him, pretending to invite him to a family reunion, and Lyric falls into the trap. It was upon this occasion that the proposition that blood is thicker than water was first put to the test...

Rhetoric goes after Lyric, with the avowed intention of "bashing him up" (archaic), but his rearguard is surprised by Metric's vanguard. Bonk! This manoeuvre is known as the Metric System.

General Electric manages to surprise Euphoric meditating on the conduct of his next few campaigns. Euphoric's morale is distinctly lowered, but he has the last word, with his famous remark, "I'll short-circuit him yet".

While Electric proclaims himself supreme chief of the Goths, to the amusement of all and sundry, it is the turn of Metric's rearguard to be surprised by Rhetoric's vanguard. Bonk! "This is bad for my system," is the comment of the exasperated Metric.

In fact, it is so bad for his system that he allows himself to be surprised by Euphoric. The battle is short and sharp. Euphoric, a wily politician, instantly proclaims himself supreme chief of the Goths. The other supreme chiefs are in fits...

MEANWHILE, OUR THREE FRIENDS ARE APPROACHING THE FRONTIER OF GAUL, WITH THEIR MINDS AT REST...

Euphoric, much annoyed, sets up camp and decides to sulk. He is surprised by Eccentric, who in his turn is attacked by Lyric, subsequently to be defeated by Electric. Electric is destined to be betrayed by Satiric, who will be beaten by Rhetoric.

Going round a corner, Rhetoric's vanguard bumps into Metric's vanguard. Bonk! Bonk! This battle is famous in the Asterixian wars as the "Battle of the Two Losers". And so the war goes on...

THE END

149